Rain

By Liza Charlesworth

ISBN: 978-1-339-02781-4

Art Director: Tannaz Fassihi; Designer: Tanya Chernyak
Photos © Getty Images and Shutterstock.com.
Copyright © Liza Charlesworth. All rights reserved. Published by Scholastic Inc.

1 2 3 4 5 6 7 8 9 10   68   32 31 30 29 28 27 26 25 24 23

Printed in Jiaxing, China. First printing, August 2023.

Is it wet and gray?
Can you see lots of drops?
Then, it's a rain day!

When it rains, dogs get wet.
Jays and snails get wet.
But do not be sad.

Rain makes plants get big.
It helps grass and trees
to stay green.

Drip, drop, plip, plop!
Rain fills up lakes and bays.
Then, we get water to drink.

Plus, it's fun to play in the rain!
You can sail a boat
in a huge puddle.

You can grab a pail
and fill it up. You can run
and jump with your sis!

Is the day wet and gray?
Be glad and not sad.
Say, "Rain, rain, stay!"